IT in construction - quantifying the benefits
Construction Industry Research and Information Association
CIRIA Report 160, 1996

Keywords
Construction industry, Information Technology, benefits, cost benefit analysis, computers

Reader Interest
Construction industry consultants, contractors, IT specialists

CLASSIFICATION	
AVAILABILITY	Unrestricted
CONTENT	Case study discussion
STATUS	Committee guided
USER	Construction sector managers, IT specialists

© CIRIA 1996

ISBN 0 86017 447 6
ISSN 0305 408X

Preface

This report was prepared by CIRIA staff, Dr S T Johnson and Mr D W Churcher, in association with Mr R W Howard and Mr D M Wager of the Construction Industry Computing Association.

The CICA provides guidance on the costs and benefits of computing and information technology through its membership and consultancy services.

Participating Organisations

The work associated with this report was carried out in partnership with a number of commercial organisations, each of which was the subject of a case study review of particular aspects of their IT procedures. CIRIA would like to thank those organisations who participated in the project for their co-operation with CIRIA and CICA in providing information for this report, without which this project would not have been possible.

Project Steering Group

The work was guided by a Steering Group which advised on the content of the report, reviewed the drafts of the report during the research period and approved the text of this publication. CIRIA wishes to express its appreciation for the work done by members of the Project Steering Group in committee and in commenting on drafts.

Dr S T Johnson (Chairman)	CIRIA
Mr J A Copley	AMEC
Mr C Gower	Babtie Group
Mr D Catton	Babtie Group
Mr D Madigan	Balfour Beatty
Mr R Crotty	Bovis Construction
Mr G Price	Christiani & Nielsen
Mr K Hendesi	Christiani & Nielsen
Mr R Thurgood	DoE Construction Sponsorship Directorate
Mr T Walker	Y J Lovell
Mr P Jackson	Mott MacDonald
Mr D Forshaw	Mott MacDonald
Mr S Vincent	Scott Wilson Kirkpatrick
Mr S Leach	Scott Wilson Kirkpatrick
Mr D W Churcher	CIRIA
Mr R W Howard	Construction Industry Computing Association
Mr D M Wager	Construction Industry Computing Association

Funding

The project was supported financially by the DoE Construction Sponsorship Directorate and CIRIA's Core Programme.

Contents

List of Figures

List of Tables

Glossary

CAD   Computer Aided Design, or Computer Aided Draughting.

EDI   Electronic Data Interchange, the protocols of formatting business data in such a way that they can be communicated electronically without requiring hard copy printout which then has to be re-keyed.

Electronic Document Management   The process of recording and managing documentation by electronic means. This can range from a database identifying each document by number, date or key word, to computer systems which can store images of the documents, translate them into computer readable form and perform searches to retrieve documents.

GDS   Computer program for computer aided draughting.

IS   Information Systems, all developed systems which have been implemented to enable electronic communication of information.

ISDN   Integrated Services Digital Network, a digital communications network available from British Telecommunications.

IT   Information Technology, all technologies associated with communication of information electronically, including computer hardware and software, communications infrastructure (cabling, etc.), communications systems.

ITT   Invitation to tender.

LAN   Local Area Network, a network of computers or terminals within a single office, allowing communication between computers and sharing of resources and peripherals.

LEAP   Computer program for structural analysis.

MOSS   Computer program for site modelling, planning, mapping etc.

OCR   Optical Character Recognition, technique for analysing images and recognising and translating the alphanumeric characters into machine-readable (usually ASCII) format.

QA   Quality Assurance.

UNIX   A computer operating system.

VAX   A computer operating system used on computers from the Digital Equipment Corporation (DEC).

1 Introduction

1.1 Scope of this report

This report considers the way in which organisations within the construction industry currently quantify the benefits they expect to obtain from any particular investment in information technology (IT). In doing so through case studies, a number of approaches are identified which might be considered or developed by others to improve the way in which decisions regarding IT investments are taken, and in general promote a more objective investment in IT.

The definition of IT is an important consideration for this report. Traditionally, information technology has been taken to mean only hardware and software. This definition has expanded as both the understanding of how technological and human resources interact and the capabilities of the technology itself have increased.

Current definitions of IT or information systems (IS) encompass technical infrastructure (e.g. cabling), communications systems (e.g. telephones, video links), any relevant specialist departments or business units and a much higher level of interaction with other employees.

This report is a summary of a series of case studies, each of which considers a single organisation and describes the approach taken to IT investment and the quantification of benefits. This approach produces snapshots of particular organisations, which are intended to provoke thought and assist in a reappraisal of existing methods within the rest of the industry. The limited number of organisations included in the study necessarily precludes any statistical analysis to generalise on the way the construction industry as a whole operates. The detailed case study analyses are included as Appendices.

1.2 Aims of the project

The aim of the project was to provide information and ideas for the construction industry as to how it might better quantify the benefits it expects to gain from its investment in information technology.

1.3 Background to the project

A survey was carried out by the Construction Industry Computing Association and KPMG Peat Marwick in 1992/3 which asked a large number of contractors and consultants for their views and experiences with information technology. This particular survey was the third in a series, undertaken at three year intervals.

One particular finding of all the surveys was that both contractors and consultants found it a problem to quantify the benefits from investment in IT. It was proposed that this difficulty meant that users of IT did not find it easy to construct a rigorous business case, through the use of cost benefit analysis, to justify a particular IT investment. This in turn meaning that the construction industry was not making the most effective investment in IT, and therefore not getting best value for money in terms of performance or business advantage.

Figure 1 below shows how the percentage of respondents to the CICA industry surveys has consistently found quantifying the benefits of IT to be a problem and that the size of the problem has tended to increase over six years:

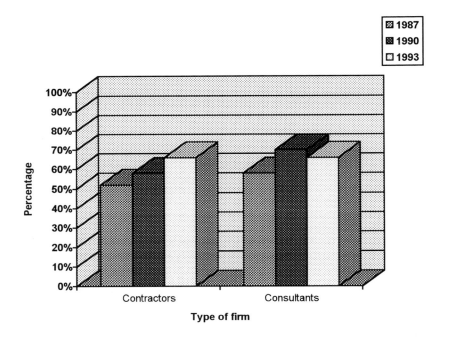

Figure 1 *Percentage of respondents who identified quantifying the benefits of IT as a problem*

In addition, the quantification of benefits is the most widespread problem over the whole industry, compared with other issues such as locating proven software, adoption of standards for the exchange of data, etc.

1.4   Methodology adopted for the project

Data was collected from the participants in the study through a series of structured interviews. These involved, where possible, a range of individuals from the organisation covering both internal service providers (e.g. IT departments) and internal service users, i.e. departments using IT to carry out their own work (design, estimating etc.).

In addition, the interviews also targeted personnel from different management levels within the organisation to gain as wide a view as possible of the organisation's approach.

The main headings under which information was collected from each participating organisation were as follows:

- Procurement procedures
- Management attitudes

- Staffing the selection/procurement process
- Budgets and cost/benefit studies
- Training
- Post implementation audit
- Information systems organisation
- Management of IT/IS
- Current systems - hardware and software
- IT/IS systems
- Development of systems
- End user support
- Networking/communications

The detailed information collected in each case study has been summarised in the Appendices 1 to 7. In addition to facts concerning each organisation's use of IT, the case studies provided qualitative information regarding the type and style of the organisation.

1.5   Attributes of participants

The scope of the study which led to this report was limited to an examination of a small number of civil/structural engineering consultants, civil engineering contractors, building contractors and a joint venture partnership between two contractors; seven case studies in total. The participants can be categorised as follows:

Table 1 *Categorisation of case study participants*

Attribute	Breakdown among participants	
Type of work	3 traditional contractors 1 management contractor 3 traditional consultants	
Size of firm	4 large	(contractors > £100M turnover, consultants > £25M fees per annum)
	3 medium	(contractors £10M - £100M, consultants £5M - £25M)
	0 small	(contractors <£10M, consultants < £5M)
Geographic spread	3 international 3 national 1 regional	
Percentage of turnover or fees spent on IT (see 1.6 on p11)	3 higher than median	(contractors > 0.25%, consultants > 1.5%)
	1 median	(contractors 0.25%, consultants 1.0-1.5%)
	1 lower than median	(contractors < 0.25%, consultants < 1.0%)
	1 don't know	
	Note: the percentage of turnover was not applicable to the joint venture project as it had a limited duration.	

1.6 Spending on information technology

Data from the Building on IT for Quality survey which indicates the percentage of turnover, for contractors, or fee income, for consultants, that is spent on IT is shown in Figure 2, below. Information technology (IT) was defined to include computer and communications hardware, software and the cost of support staff.

Each band of expenditure is plotted against the percentage of those responding who fell within the band.

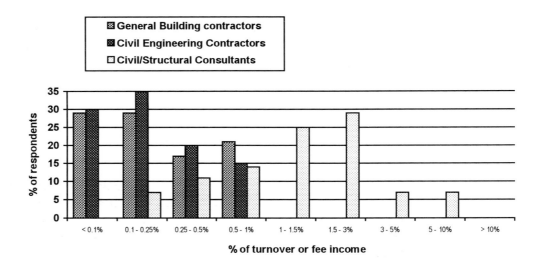

Figure 2 *Percentage spending on IT by industry sector (Building on IT for Quality, CICA/KPMG)*

From the data collected by CICA/KPMG, the median ranges of expenditure were calculated as follows:

General building/civil engineering contractors   0.25% of turnover
Civil/Structural consultants   1.0-1.5% of fee income

These have been used as comparisons for the figures derived from the case study participants and in the profile in section 1.5 above.

2   Discussion of survey results

2.1   Introduction

The case studies are included in this report as Appendices. The following discussion is based on the information contained within them.

The discussion refers to how the type of business, whether a consultant or contractor, affects the way benefits are quantified.

However, it is recognised that IT strategies are often closely linked to the overall business strategy of an organisation. This section does not set out to provide guidance on general management strategies or to discuss the way each of the case study participants is managed.

2.2   Assessing costs and benefits

The study has indicated that organisations use a variety of procedures to assess the costs and benefits of any proposed IT investment. These can vary from those who carry out detailed studies to consider all the issues relating to costs and identified benefits, through those who prepare less detailed or informal assessments to those who carry out no specific assessments.

Table 2 *Types of cost/benefit assessment identified in the case studies*

Formal	Provides information for informed decisions on the proposed implementation of new systems. Can be expensive and time consuming. Can provide the basis for post implementation monitoring of success.
Informal	More suitable where existing systems are being replaced or where the cost of carrying out a formal benefit study would be excessive compared with the cost of the IT investment.
No specific assessment	Would be used where circumstances require specific systems to be implemented for other than direct financial gain.

Table 2 summarises the situations where each particular form of assessment might be used, based on the experiences of the case studies. Aspects relating to the choice and selection of assessment procedures are discussed below.

2.2.1 Options for assessing the benefits of IT

Several approaches to the assessment of costs and benefits associated with IT investment have come out of the case studies, ranging from none at all, through informal studies, to formal managed and validated cost benefit analysis.

No specific assessment

There are some situations where a formal structured assessment is either not possible or necessary, although this might seem to go against good business practice. From the case studies, these include:

1. Project driven IT: e.g. the client for a particular project has required that a particular IT system be used. The costs will be built into the fee or price quoted or included as a provisional sum in the contract. The risk of not taking this path will be exclusion from the selection process. This method imposed by the client will favour organisations who already have or are familiar with the systems required as this will enable them to submit a lower bid.

2. Minor investments: e.g. the cost of the IT required is so small that the cost of carrying out any assessment would be a significant factor to be weighed against the benefits to be gained.

Informal assessment

Although limited in their scope and usefulness, informal assessments are generally quick and relatively cheap to carry out. The assessment focuses on those costs and benefits which are easily quantified or qualified.

Informal assessments have an increased risk of being inaccurate because not all the possible costs and benefits are identified and assessed. They are best used in cases where the scope for major error is reduced, for example, when assessing a modest investment or where others' experiences are generally positive.

Formal cost benefit analysis

The evidence from the case studies suggests that this is the least common method of appraising IT investments. The complexity of carrying out a full cost benefit analysis which has both the breadth of information and sufficient detail to be meaningful makes it a major exercise.

However, information on the costs and benefits of any system may be required by the directors, partners or those responsible for the financial aspects of an organisation, to help them with decisions on whether or not to make an investment.

The examples given in the case studies, of the telephone system and the project IT strategy, illustrate some important features:

- there may be costs and benefits which cannot be quantified, and cannot be included in the mathematical part of the cost benefit analysis. They may still be significant and must not be excluded or otherwise overlooked because of this

- alternatively, it may be decided that all costs and benefits can be assigned a value. The difficulty of calculating these and the levels of confidence placed in them will vary. In order to compare like with like, costs and benefits can only be directly compared when they have been derived with the same confidence. One way of reducing all costs and benefits to an equal level of confidence is to apply a percentage confidence level to the absolute cost or benefit, as indicated in the joint venture case study in Appendix 4.

Formal cost benefit analyses are time consuming to carry out and the results need to be seen in the context of the confidence with which the various estimates have been made. There is a danger that too much credence will be placed on any numerical result that is produced without looking at the basis upon which that figure has been calculated.

However, these analyses can be a useful tool to assess the feasibility of any project and be the basis on which IT investment may be justified. A formal analysis can also provide a benchmark from which to measure the success of the IT implementation.

2.2.2 Quantitative and qualitative benefits

Broadly speaking, both costs and benefits break down into those that can be quantified and those that can not. In practice, the ease or difficulty with which costs or benefits can be quantified is a continuous range and depends on a number of factors. There will always be costs or benefits which can not be quantified at all and these are frequently the most difficult to take into account in any analysis, which tends to focus on numerical assessment. In addition, there will always be costs or benefits which were not foreseen when the analysis was carried out.

Table 3 *Examples of costs and benefits and how easy they are to quantify*

Ease or difficulty of quantifying costs/benefits	Costs (examples)	Benefits (examples)
Easier to quantify . . . . More difficult to quantify Impossible to quantify	Hardware, software - purchase and maintenance Recruitment of specialist staff Additional facilities/office requirements Training costs Reassessment of business plan or objectives now possible due to IT Costs originally unforeseen	Improvements in productivity and reduction in direct costs e.g. wages Savings over existing systems e.g. reduced maintenance costs Reduction in facilities/office requirements Changes in working practices, assuming these are beneficial Possible improvement in company image and perception of clients Benefits originally unforeseen

2.2.3 Examples from the case studies

The seven case studies have demonstrated different approaches to the problem of how to analyse the costs and benefits that are associated with any particular investment in information technology.

In some instances, no cost benefit studies were carried out, whilst some organisations have spent long periods of time preparing detailed studies.

Table 4, below, gives some of the alternatives that were found for assessing costs or benefits under broadly similar circumstances.

Table 4 *Examples of analysis carried out for different types of IT investment*

Type of potential investment	Examples of how cost and/or benefit is quantified *(drawn from the case studies)*		
	Formal analysis	Informal analysis	No analysis
Item of hardware or software		Informal (check that suggested item matches current policy and future requirements)	No analysis (expenditure either too small or analysis previously carried out)
Computer system (admin.)	Formal cost benefit analysis (carried out by external consultant with in-house IT/User group)		No analysis (system too critical for cost to be a sensitive issue)
	Formal cost benefit analysis (identifying 5 year cash flows and qualitative benefits)		No analysis (judgement based on previous experience - joint venture project taking advice from JV partner)
Computer system (technical)	Formal cost benefit analysis (not able to justify on quantifiable benefit alone)	Informal (heads of departments with user group assessed needs and considered risks of new system)	No analysis (benefits assessed by period of trial usage)
	Formal (strategic evaluation considering both IT and business benefits)	Informal (system procurement driven by project requirements)	
IT strategy	Formal cost benefit analysis (costs and savings identified - confidence levels applied to savings to measure the 'less quantifiable' benefits)		

2.3   Conclusions from the case studies

The case studies have provided some very different views of how construction organisations assess and quantify the benefits they expect to obtain from their investment in information technology and systems.

The approach of sampling a small number of organisations in detail has provided insight into how IT is procured and integrated, with benefit, into the work environment.

The conclusions of this study are as follows:

2.3.1   The need for and benefits of carrying out quantified cost benefit studies

There are two main approaches to assessing the benefits of IT:

- Formal and/or quantitative cost benefit analyses
- Informal and/or qualitative assessment of costs and benefits

A third option is to do nothing - not to consider costs or benefits at all.

Although some organisations successfully use a form of analysis or assessment to implement a successful IT strategy, this is not a prerequisite. Equally, carrying out formal cost benefits analyses will not, on their own, result in an effective strategy.

It is a difficult and complex task to produce a meaningful cost benefit study that will predict with confidence and accuracy the costs and benefits associated with a particular investment and the effort required must not be underestimated. The cost of carrying out the cost benefit study itself should be weighed against the scale of possible net benefits.

The nature of cost benefit analyses and the numerical methods available tend to make them more applicable to cases where a large proportion of the costs and benefits can be quantified accurately and there are few unquantifiable costs or benefits. This tends to apply in cases of system substitution, where the information technology is replacing existing manual systems or updating existing IT.

Systems which introduce new areas of business or have a wider effect on the operation of the organisation, and which therefore have a higher proportion of costs and benefits which cannot be quantified, are more likely to be assessed using informal methods.

Perhaps one of the advantages of attempting a formal or even informal cost-benefit analysis is having to make explicit the various assumptions and conditions necessary for the investment to work. This transparency is important in convincing others about investments in or spending on IT.

2.3.2   Other influences driving the implementation of IT

Information technology is introduced into organisations for a number of reasons:

- business strategy predicts the need for particular IT solutions to assist the organisation in meeting its corporate goals - there is a strong case for carrying out formal or informal cost benefit studies

- a client requires that a particular IT solution is adopted for his project - although this might be negotiable, it is a strong prerequisite to the contract being awarded - there is little or no choice but to adopt the required IT, costs must be assessed and included in the contract fee but no assessment of benefits is required. This has been noted as a particular trend among consultants

- core business functions could not sensibly be carried out any other way, for example in completing some structural engineering calculations there may be no other choice than to use IT. However comparative assessments of alternative systems will be needed.

In some instances, such as project specific IT, the decision is already made by the client's requirements and it is on the basis of wider business strategies that IT is purchased.

2.3.3 Consultation, ownership and audits

Additional factors which contribute to the successful implementation of IT strategy and specific systems are:

- a consultation process, either through a formal user group or IT committee, to collect information from representatives of all the appropriate staff. It is important that end users and line managers are included in this process

- full support for the use of IT from Directors and senior managers, one of whom is directly identified with the specification and implementation of each new system. In practice, the operation of this role might be delegated to a specific 'project manager' from the relevant user department

- post implementation audits for each new system or item of hardware or software, to provide feedback to the procurement process and information to the organisation as a whole on the performance of new items of hardware and software.

2.3.4 Other elements of IT strategy identified by the case studies

Computer/IT Steering Committees and User Groups are an effective way of involving representatives from all relevant departments as well as staff from different levels within the organisation and may be used either for formulating policy or advising those making decisions of the views of the organisation.

The rapid development of IT has resulted in individual items of hardware and software being seen more and more as commodity items which are differentiated principally by price and less so by performance. The quality of the items and the degree to which they are 'fit for purpose' is becoming a lesser issue as the available products improve in performance and functionality.

IT investment within an organisation tends to follow a cycle of alternating evolutionary and radical advancement. Major reviews, which may result in a total rethink of IT policy, are undertaken at intervals of several years (typically five to ten). Between these reviews, advances in IT are absorbed on an evolutionary basis, fitting in with the broad policies from the last major review. In some instances, five years of evolution may represent more change than a revolutionary re-thinking of IT strategy, whether measured in level of investment, manpower activity or any other unit of measurement.

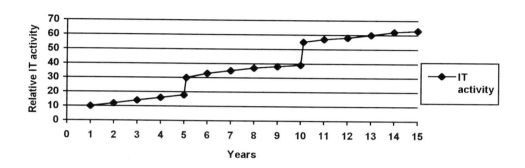

Figure 3 *Evolutionary and revolutionary advances in IT*

Within contractors, the trend has been to move from a central IT department serving all the computing needs of the organisation, to a more distributed approach where each of the operating units has control of its own computing, within strategy guidelines defined, controlled and supported by a small central IT unit. The evaluation and quantification of any costs and benefits and the responsibility of implementation would be with the operating unit.

Much of the actual cost of an IT implementation is not in the cost of the hardware and software, but the ancillary cost of staff time, training, support costs, etc. These are not always reflected fully in cost/benefit studies.

Although the benefits of any IT system may be clearly understood at the feasibility and implementation stages, it has been found that additional and unforeseen benefits sometimes accrue. This was found to be the case, for example, with an electronic mail implementation where improved communications exceeded all expectations and use quickly expanded.

Any change in management procedures within an organisation carries associated risks. The benefits and effectiveness of an IT implementation is dependent upon the control and management of risk. One of the case studies shows how an organisation has identified and assessed the risks involved with its IT strategy (Appendix 4) and this demonstrates the range of significant risks to the successful implementation of the technology. These include risks with regard to the function and timeliness of the technology, the responses of the users to the technology and the rate of change within the business environment as a whole. These are illustrated in Figure 4. The weights given to the different risks will depend on the nature of the organisation and its IT history.

The top ten risks identified in the case study in Appendix 4 divided into these three categories in the following proportions:

Technology risks (including budgets)	4 out of 10
User reception risks	4 out of 10
Business environment risks	2 out of 10.

Figure 4 *Risks to implementing successful IT strategies*

3 Good practice for quantifying the benefits of IT

3.1 Introduction

Information technology is recognised as a much wider field, including many new issues, than the traditional view of 20 years ago. The newer considerations, relating to human interaction and staff issues with regard to IT have been shown to be those which are least readily quantifiable, both in terms of the benefits that IT can bring and in terms of the costs that any new system will have.

Recognition that these issues exist is the first step in forming a more complete picture of the effect of any investment in IT on the organisation as a whole. From the results of the case studies, there are many individual actions that can be taken by an organisation's management to improve the chances of implementing a successful IT strategy. It is not possible to prescribe particular ingredients without reference to the culture and management style of the organisation.

The following section provides checklists as aides memoires for the procurement of IT and in particular with regard for the identification and, where possible, quantification, of benefits and costs to the organisation.

3.2 Checklists for quantifying the benefits of IT

The following points are extracted from the experiences of the case study organisations and are intended to provide guidance for organisations assessing a possible implementation of information technology.

Table 5 lists the most significant questions to be asked in any cost/benefit assessment, regardless of complexity or degree of formality. Table 6 lists considerations which it might be relevant to take into account when carrying out a cost/benefit assessment.

It is suggested that checklists of this type be used as the basis for company specific guidelines and procedures.

Table 5 *Guidelines for assessment of potential IT investments*

Define what you mean by IT	An agreed definition of what is covered by the term IT is vital. For example, does it include hardware, software, infrastructure, dedicated staff, training, maintenance, support ? How wide is the definition - computers, cables, networks, data/telephone systems, all electronic communication ?
Who is involved in the consultation process ?	This should be defined for each project, and might include any or all of the following: 　　　　IT staff 　　　　directors/partners/managers 　　　　end users 　　　　maintenance staff 　　　　finance staff 　　　　human resources staff.
Who signs off the system specification, following the consultation ?	Responsibility for systems is vested in the appropriate directors or senior managers through ownership of the installed technology and a requirement to sign off the specification. Individual project managers with day-to-day responsibility should be appointed from the user department.
What are the criteria for success (and/or failure) ?	It is very important that these should be defined and agreed as part of the system specification. These measures will need to be assessed following implementation to assess whether a system has succeeded or failed and lessons learned for future projects.
How are costs and benefits assessed ?	Costs and benefits can either be directly quantified (at an assumed confidence level of 100%), or can be assessed and then assigned a percentage confidence level (between 0-100%). Alternatively, informal and qualitative lists of costs and benefits can be compiled and compared to arrive at an overall judgement of net cost or net benefit. Or, a judgement might be made that the cost of a cost benefit analysis is disproportionate compared to the value of the IT investment.
Post-implementation audit	The system should be judged against the pre-determined criteria for success or failure, see above. Instances where systems do not meet specification may lead to changes in procedures for selection and assessment.

Table 6 *Considerations to make in assessing or quantifying the costs and benefits of IT*

Possible costs *	Possible benefits *
Quoted costs of hardware and software (dependent on breadth of definition of IT)	Savings from fewer staff, less office space, less administrative support
Costs of additional staff/upgrading staff	Cheaper operational costs leading to either greater profit margins or larger turnover from competitive pricing or a combination of the two
Costs of additional offices, support	
Training - immediate users as well as medium and long-term	Improved company image with clients and public compared to competitors
Maintenance of new hardware and software support, cost of consumables	Better staff morale from elimination of mundane activities
Exchange of data from existing systems (manual or computer based)	Income from new services offered to clients
Maintenance of archive material	Better information (more consistent, more accurate, more precise, generated more quickly, etc.) allowing better business decisions to be made
Finance of any borrowing or lost opportunity cost of capital	

* Not all the items listed as costs and benefits will apply to every IT investment.

4 Conclusions and the need for further research

The objective of this study was to provide information to organisations involved in construction on how the benefits obtained from implementing information technology may be quantified in order for better and more informed choices to be made.

The study was seen very much as a first phase, feasibility study to determine some costs and benefits and their quantification; and to identify other issues that will require further investigation. The following are suggested as topics needing more detailed investigation.

- In terms of scope, these investigations were limited to seven organisations and can be seen as only scratching the surface of this topic. Although much useful information was drawn out of the case studies, it is suggested that a study involving more organisations would give a more representative picture.

- Some of the organisations participating in the study use formal cost benefit methods. It would be helpful to identify a greater number of these to enable detailed benchmarking.

- The study identified that the growth of computing and information technology within organisations is frequently in cycles of evolution and revolution. Further investigation to establish the effect this has on the industry would be beneficial.

- Implementing IT in joint venture partnerships would seem to create its own problems. It is suggested that study should be made of how companies procure and implement information technology on joint venture projects.

- Further investigations and comparisons should be made between UK organisations, other countries in the European Union and those outside the EU to evaluate how benefits are assessed and how practices and results compare with the UK.

Appendix 1 Building contractor (1)

A1.1 Introduction

This is a building company with a turnover of about £400m per annum. They carry out a range of building work and the organisation is structured to reflect this. The construction division deals with new work, repairs and maintenance, refurbishment, and plant hire; there is a division dealing with partnership schemes with housing associations and local authorities, and a homes division. Overseas projects are handled by a separate division.

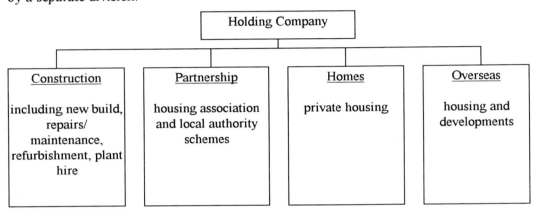

A1.2 Overview of computing strategy

The group had for many years had a central data processing department running a main frame computer serving all the companies, much of the software being developed and maintained with in-house expertise. There was considerable confusion concerning responsibilities for computing between the group and the divisions, and little or no co-ordination between them for IT spending on the central mainframe computer and the distributed PC systems.

In 1989 it was decided to invite management consultants to review their computing and to suggest improvements. Following this a formal strategy was drawn up, which they started to implement in 1990. The main thrust of the new strategy was to devolve the responsibility and control of IT to the user divisions. The ultimate responsibility for IT decisions rests with the main board, however, in practice it is dealt with by a committee of the chief executives of all the companies in the group.

A group information systems (IS) department was created to plan and control the overall computing strategies, especially in areas such as communications, networking, and standards; and to provide a service to the holding company for the consolidation of group accounts for statutory purposes and to maintain the group accounting, payroll/personnel, and other systems. The position of Group IS Director was established to co-ordinate and control divisional activities.

The central IS department has a staff of six people and each of the main operating companies has an IS manager, or a nominated person with computing responsibilities. There are 10 IT staff in these companies.

There is a group IS steering committee chaired by the Group IS Director which meets six-monthly to direct the general computing and communications strategy. This committee is made up of the Group IS Director and other selected directors and chief executives from the operating companies.

An IS Managers' group meets monthly with the IS Director to discuss group issues, standards, to share problems, and to learn of systems, developments and other activities in the companies. Where there are issues of a general nature requiring further investigation, such as document management, communications, etc. an *ad hoc* working group will also be set up.

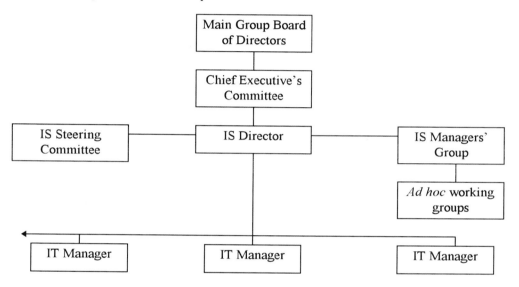

It is important to the company that both management and users participate at all stages in the working parties to consider possible systems and that they are involved in the selection and implementation of any systems. When they were considering the financial and accounting systems for the construction company, surveyors, buyers and other non-financial staff were on the working party.

They consider that any time and additional costs are more than covered by the benefits when the systems are implemented. This has been borne out by the interest now being shown by the surveyors, buyers and managers in accessing the contract costing information available from the accounting system.

Key Elements of the IS Strategy

- Central Strategy
- Devolved Responsibility
- Any implementation must improve the working efficiency
- Formal cost benefit studies carried out

A1.3   Overview of computer systems

The commitment of director and senior manager towards the use of computing has changed in recent years. There is now generally a positive attitude to the investment in communications, IT and information systems. The annual expenditure on IT/IS is in the range 0.5 to 0.7% of the company turnover. This certainly reflects well against the median spend identified in the CICA/KPMG survey. The number of terminals per head of staff within the group is also high with almost 90% of administration staff with access to a terminal. This figure is rather less for technical staff, where there are about 100 screens to 300 staff. The construction company has somewhat less screens to numbers of staff, with about 62% of administration staff having access to screens.

The central IS group have established guidelines within which the operating companies can develop their strategies and systems. There is generally a single source of supply for hardware, maintenance, training, etc., this gives the advantages of arranging beneficial purchasing agreements and having one point of contact for support.

There is a rigid central policy towards networking and network standards. Each office has its own local area network (LAN) with an average of about 90% of the computers linked to these LAN's

As with many other construction companies, computer-based accounting and costing systems have been used for many years and have become accepted as essential for the organisation. Computing for technical applications and site use are either not used, or less well established. Although the need for computing to assist those technical areas has been identified, the company is not yet satisfied that the benefits of implementation will outweigh the costs.

To reduce development costs it was decided that where possible, packaged software solutions should be used rather than continuing with in-house development. However, there are several in-house systems which need to be supported until such time as alternative systems are implemented.

The policy of distributed computing allows each operating company to identify and choose software to suit their own particular requirements. In practice this means that companies are likely to acquire different systems for one application. This has proved to be the case for several applications, including accounting and cost control, estimating, project planning, etc.

There is a move towards the implementation of Windows applications. For this reason it seems likely that some divisions will, in future, use the range of products in the Microsoft office integrated system.

A1.4   Cost benefit studies

It is the general policy that formal cost benefit studies will be carried out for any proposed IS or IT investment. A typical study is likely to have the following elements:

- Main scope of the proposal
- Any likely operational and procedural changes
- A summary of the main perceived benefits

- A detailed cost benefit analysis
- Details of any subjective benefits not costed
- Conclusion and recommendations

The calculation of costs will include all the IT elements, including hardware, software, communications, staffing costs, training, maintenance, implementation, etc., both as an initial capital cost and an ongoing/running cost. Consideration will be given to the period over which the implementation is to be written off, three to five years depending on the type of system being implemented.

The likely financial savings that can be identified if the proposals were implemented are calculated. These would include savings such as staffing, accommodation, stationery, hardware and maintenance costs, improvements in efficiency, etc.

In addition there may be some subjective benefits that are more difficult to quantify. These would be identified and listed as benefits, but with no financial value associated with them. These are likely to be benefits such as:

Better information	allowing quicker decision making by managers; decisions to be taken by line managers where information may now be available; and, less time spent on reconciling information or queries from the system.
Cash flow	improved cash flow would lead to better cash management.
Staffing	improved job satisfaction, less time off for sickness, fewer staff changes. Removal of some of the menial tasks in a job.
Image	improving the image of the organisation to provide a more marketable organisation and therefore the opportunity to carry out more prestigious or profitable work.
Improved efficiency	the provision of better data promptly will provide operational efficiencies making the organisation more profitable.
Other similar benefits	

When completed the proposal and cost benefit study would be presented to the Chief Executive's Committee for approval.

A1.5 Computer systems in detail

The following are some examples of particular systems being used within the group and the approaches used for their selection and implementation.

A1.5.1 Accounting

Until two or three years ago the accounting for all the companies was dealt with centrally using in-house developed software. This had become outdated and needed completely rewriting, or to be replaced by a new package or bespoke software. The group policy dictated that where possible any change should be to package software.

Following periods of detailed investigation and evaluation by each of the operating companies, systems were selected, proposals to change including detailed cost and benefit analyses were put to the boards, and new systems implemented. System selection was co-ordinated by the group IS department, although consideration was given to choosing similar systems the Homes, and Partnership divisions chose different software to that selected by the Construction division. The housing companies identifying that their requirements for plot/site costing differed from those of construction, where the need was for a more extensive contract costing system.

In addition, the group services company were looking for different functionality from their accounting system with less emphasis on the specific construction and contract costing modules, but needed to deal efficiently with inter company charging, and required improved report writing facilities; a third and different system was chosen. The plant hire company has not changed systems yet and is using the rather old in-house developed system, although this is now dealt with as a bureau service by external facilities managers.

This means that four different accounting systems are being used by the group. However, only limited interfacing is required between systems for payroll and consolidation.

Another package is used by group services to deal with consolidation, figures being transferred by electronic means from the operating company accounting system, or spreadsheets directly to the consolidation system. The short time scale for selecting a system to deal with consolidation meant that there were no formal evaluation and selection procedures. Management consultants recommended a package based upon the specification, although other systems were also evaluated.

A1.5.2 Human resource

The integrated payroll and personnel system is run centrally by group services and provided as a service to the operating companies. The system originally ran on the company mainframe; although the bespoke system was rather cumbersome, it had been used successfully for several years. Prior to the decision to move from the mainframe, an earlier attempt had been made to introduce package software. In 1986 the company first decided to move from their in-house system to a package solution. However the package chosen and implemented was not satisfactory, it did not have the necessary functionality and was too slow. The company reverted to the old bespoke system after a few months.

Following the decision to migrate from the mainframe a working party was set up in 1991 with representatives from payroll, personnel, IT and finance, and management consultants to help with the selection and implementation of the system. They looked for a system that would be able to integrate both payroll and personnel activities, considering both package solutions and the use of an external bureau service.

The working group and consultants went through an evaluation and selection procedure, sending out invitations to tender in March 1992. This produced a shortlist of five which was eventually cut down to two possible systems. Further demonstrations and investigations were carried out before a final selection was made. A detailed cost benefit analysis was prepared as part of the proposal that was submitted to the board for approval.

A package system was chosen and implemented in November 1992 with the intention of starting to use it in earnest the following April. However, problems arose when trying to use the system, and it became clear that what was being sold by the software house was a 'package of tools' rather than a fully developed payroll package. Both the software house and the company needed to put in considerable IT resource to further develop the system. The transfer to the new payroll system was delayed, eventually going 'live' in May.

Further problems were found and it took some while for users to be confident with the payroll systems. The personnel application was not implemented until several months later. The series of problems arising from the implementation of the system identified a number of issues:

- the original ITT sought one supplier for hardware and software - these criteria were changed during the procurement procedure. Problems arose between the hardware used and the software supplied, which needed to be resolved.
- the working party and consultants had been misled into believing that there was an established payroll/personnel system. No one should assume that just because they are shown something in a demonstration that it is necessarily part of an established system.
- payroll, particularly weekly payroll, is a critical application and is probably one of the most difficult for a contractor to specify and implement.

A1.5.3 Estimating

A working party to investigate estimating systems was set up early 1993, the needs of the department identified and a questionnaire sent out to six or seven system suppliers. The responses were assessed, and the working party went to see demonstrations of selected systems. Following further discussions it was decided that no firm decision could be made to purchase any of the packages. However it was agreed that the preferred system should be implemented for a trial period of three months (subsequently extended to five months). Hardware was purchased as this could be used elsewhere if it was eventually decided not to proceed with full implementation after the trial. Software training was provided by the software supplier at a fee.

The trial went well, although at the end of the period no decision was made to implement the system at that stage. They have now decided to look at the other available systems again to see whether they should opt for another system, implement the trialled system, or continue with existing procedures.

A1.5.4 Communications

Communications are seen as an important element in the rapid and regular flow of information between offices, and between offices and sites. A central and key factor in the control of communications with the head office is now in place with the replacement of the main switchboard with a new digital switch. This will allow the organisation to make the most of the emerging opportunities supported by Integrated Services Digital Network (ISDN) and other technologies.

A study of the requirements and the available systems was carried out by a working party and a cost benefit analysis prepared for the directors before the decision was taken to implement the new system.

A1.6 Conclusions

When the IT strategy was prepared, it was envisaged that the integration of information within the various systems would be a longer-term priority. Multi-phase projects were established in each division with the prime aim of moving systems quickly from the costly mainframe, which was to be disposed of. Links are now in place between divisional accounting systems and the group inter-company, payroll and consolidation systems. Further stages are now being implemented to introduce new modules of the integrated software packages.

The use of computers on sites is very limited, where they exist they are generally stand-alone PC's. A few sites have local area networks (LANs), the major site-based LAN implementation is on a 'cost plus' contract where its use has been encouraged by the client.

It is planned to link the larger sites with offices. There would be a number of advantages if this is done, sites would have more access to the purchasing department, purchasing and invoice queries could be resolved on screen etc. The cost justification for this has not yet been found, and a two- to three-year timescale is considered realistic.

The decision to downsize from a mainframe to several UNIX machines has been considered successful. When computing was offered as a central mainframe service to the operating companies there was limited interest in the way this was done, however, since the computing responsibility has been devolved to each division, management attitudes have changed with directors and managers being more concerned that the most efficient and cost effective systems are used.

Appendix 2 Building contractor (2)

A2.1 Introduction

The second case study of a building contractor is a company with a turnover approaching £100m. There is a head office and six regional offices. The company undertakes a wide range of building activities, with subsidiary companies dealing with housing, etc.

The Board of Directors consists of the Managing Director, Financial Director, Operations Directors, and a Commercial Director. The Commercial Director being responsible for providing the support services of estimating, legal, procurement, and computing and information technology to all the operating units.

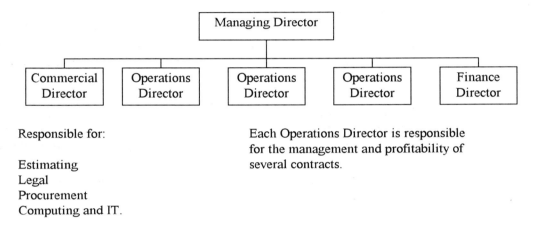

Responsible for:

Estimating
Legal
Procurement
Computing and IT.

Each Operations Director is responsible for the management and profitability of several contracts.

A2.2 Overview of computing strategy

Considerable emphasis has been placed on the implementation and use of computers on sites. It has been identified that the control of site information is important and that information handling on sites, and between sites and offices, is well managed, and a key to the profitability of the company.

With the increase in the size and value of sites more information is being handled and similar information is being used by several people who frequently input the same information for their own use, thus duplicating work and increasing the chance of errors.

The computer systems were running under the UNIX operating system, however the computing strategy changed and in an attempt to improve the user interface it was decided that there would be a move to Microsoft Windows.

A large investment has been made in site computing in recent years. This year a capital expenditure of £800,000 is planned for site computing alone. Site computer installations are financed by each individual project; the cost of any hardware, licence the software, and for maintenance, support, training and help desk as used.

A2.3 Overview of computing systems

The company have a core construction industry accounting system for the statutory financial requirements, management accounts. Other applications, particularly the procurement and site computing systems have been developed as in-house with links into the accounting system.

Proprietary software has been purchased for applications such as project planning and control, Computer Aided Design (CAD), structural analysis and design of temporary works, etc.

A2.4 Computer systems in detail

A2.4.1 Site computing

It was decided that a company needed a standard suite of programs for site-based functions. The software market was investigated to identify any potential packages, but none were found to be suitable. Those that were available were considered to be too trivial and did few of the functions required. The approaches adopted by the systems for project control and change control were not those in use by the company. The packages were also too structured and did not lend themselves to be easily changed. Integration between the various functions required was regarded as an important issue, the time, cost and effort needed to modify the packages could not be justified. The decision was made to develop an in-house system, in the belief that it would be more efficient. No formal quantification of the benefits of implementing a system was done.

The system running under the UNIX operating system, was developed over a period of two years, with more than seven man years of effort in its production, and was implemented on all sites.

When the decision was taken to move to the Windows graphical user interface, the systems had to be re-written; a task which took one programmer less than a year to complete. The aspects covered by the site systems include the following function:

- Drawing control - a drawing and document register, giving the facility of holding images of drawings where this is considered beneficial.
- Information control - the management of architects and site instructions, requests for information, etc.
- Financial control - a whole range of functions from the initial cost plan and cash flows, through to the management of the financial aspects, such as valuations and reporting.
- Snagging system - details of defects, production of snagging lists, their management and resolution.
- Quality management systems.

Working groups, with both managers and users, were set up to identify the needs of each of the main functions. They reviewed the system specification and met on a regular basis to comment on the program development as it proceeded. When complete, each module was tested on six sites. A trial of the whole system was implemented on a pilot site, followed by a full implementation programme.

A2.4.2 Office systems

Having concentrated in recent years on the development of site-based systems, they are now looking more closely at the systems used in the office. Following the decision to move the development of some of the application packages to the Windows environment, the company decided to adopt the Microsoft Office integrated suite of packages as standard and available to all users, thus giving the opportunity to provide the following general applications to users:

Word-processing:	Word
Spreadsheet:	Excel
E-Mail:	MS Mail
Presentation:	Powerpoint
Database:	Access
Project Management:	Microsoft Project

No formal study was carried out to quantify the benefits of using the Microsoft Office suite of programs.

Implementation of Microsoft Office is already underway, starting with the secretarial skills, this will be followed by the technical staff. All staff using the new system will receive specific training.

A2.4.3 Accounting

The Company had, for about 15 years, used a bureau to deal with its accounting function. This system had become dated and was considered rather crude when compared with other systems available. There had been some updating, but little system development in recent years. The decision was taken that the accounting activity should be upgraded.

A small study group was set up to investigate the options. The auditors were consulted to advise on the requirements of the system, and the in-house IT department discussed the technical issues. Any new system should run under UNIX, be developed in a fourth generation language (4GL), and be able to interface with spreadsheet packages. It should also be able to run on dumb terminal and PCs and be able to deal with the coding structures already established.

A shortlist of three systems was established, based on the functional and technical requirements, and there were discussions with the suppliers on the specification of customisation required. The study group carried out an evaluation of the shortlisted systems to make a selection. Customisation of the system was an issue requiring careful consideration as the software houses tended to underplay the extent of any tailoring that was necessary to their systems, and therefore the cost of this work.

Some thought was given to the costs and benefits of the systems, although no formal study of the quantification of benefit was carried out. Savings were found in the bureau changes, and a reduction in the number of staff needed to input the data. It was found that there would be a return on capital in less than five years. Other benefits included more information readily available and better reporting facilities to produce regular and *ad hoc* reports.

It was also considered that using an in-house system would allow more control of the system and its future development, than would be the case if a bureau service was retained.

An accountant with IT skills was appointed to project manage the system implementation.

A period of six months was allowed for the specification and development of the customisation features, and three months to transfer data to the new system. The new system went 'live' mid year, with no parallel running of the old system, although the bureau was maintained until the end of the year.

A2.4.4 Procurement

The procurement system is seen as having close links with the site systems. The function of procurement is driven by sites and the latest, the third generation of procurement system, is intended to remove the transfer of paper between sites and the office-based buying department. It allows site managers to access the central procurement system and download information necessary for its use and manipulation, and place orders where possible.

The latest version of the system has recently been rewritten in-house in the Windows environment. Before the development of the new system took place, the head of procurement talked to buyers in other contractor organisations to determine the systems they used and, while there was an investigation of available packages, none were considered suitable.

A user group was established to set out the requirements of the new system, to work with the IT department during the development phase, and to test the system on completion.

The benefits of the procurement system are:

- to provide information to managers to improve buying standards
- to provide support to business processes so that buying can be done more efficiently
- as a major player the company would be seen to be at the leading edge
- selling the business processes to outside markets, and
- an opportunity to reduce risks, and then to manage them.

One of the key aspects that has attempted to be built into the system is that of risk management. The accounting system is a historical record of transactions that have been completed. The procurement system must enable managers to assess the risk before placing an order with a specific subcontractor or supplier.

The justification for investing in the development of this latest procurement system was that it would reduce the risks to the company by holding better information on subcontractors and suppliers, and on the risk in using them. Also the system allows people to buy more effectively and more efficiently.

Although consideration was given to quantifying the benefits of IT, no formal exercise was carried out. The Board of Directors, who make the decision to proceed with any IT development, look to the heads of the departments concerned as their 'experts' to justify a computer system. It is anticipated that the pay-back period for the procurement system will be two years.

It is anticipated that the move to use this system on-site will improve site efficiency and reduce the need for in the office based procurement staff. It is anticipated that the system can be used by other companies in the group, and sold or licensed, thus sharing the development costs.

A2.5 Conclusions

The types of projects undertaken by this company allow for more of the management activities to be dealt with at site level. For this reason they have identified the need to provide more site systems and better communications between sites and offices. Recent IT investment has been directed towards the improvement of site systems.

Formal cost benefit studies are rarely done, but this would not seem to have much impact on their ability to implement effective computer systems.

Support for innovation from the Board of Directors is allowing the company to look again at the construction process, and the management of information, to see how business re-engineering might improve the efficiency of the organisation.

Appendix 3 Civil engineering contractor (1)

A3.1 Introduction

This company carries out civil engineering work both in the UK and overseas. The study has looked at the UK only, where there is an annual turnover in the region of £80m for 1994. A wide range of civil engineering work is carried out including roads, bridges, harbour and marine, refineries, etc., together with associated building work, and some development projects.

In the UK there are five regional offices and about 30 active sites. The main computing facility is at a central location where all the accounting, costing and administrative functions are dealt with. Most of the computing expertise is also at this central location where there are a small number of staff responsible for any in-house development and IT support.

The question of IT expenditure is always difficult to compare since each organisation uses different criteria to analyse spend. However this company would seem to spend just under 0.20% of their turnover on IT. This is less than the median for contractors of 0.25% given in the CICA/KPMG report *Building on IT for Quality*. The company look for a return on capital for IT expenditure in three years, whilst larger more expensive IT investments are written off over a five to seven year period. Where the cost of site computing is less than £20,000, it is generally written off against the project at the time of purchase.

A3.2 Overview of computing strategy

Established procedures are well documented for all aspects of the business, including computing. The company has a centralised management approach to computing with a Computer Steering Group (CSG) to act as a focal point for the implementation of the IT strategy and training, all IT expenditure must be sanctioned by the group. The composition of the CSG is similar to the management board, to whom it reports, and also includes the IT Manager.

Each computer system has a sponsor, usually one of the directors. The sponsor is responsible for setting out the requirements obtaining approval from the CSG, and taking steps to progress a project in accordance with agreed timescales and budgets. The sponsor appoints a computer project manager who deals with the detailed planning and development of a project, including the costs for the project, recurring costs such as maintenance costs etc., together with the outline implementation plan, and the business benefits, wherever possible quantified, together with a statement of justification for the project.

The company has a policy of using packages wherever possible, however there are established bespoke systems developed over the last eight years, and some of these systems are currently being modified or rewritten in-house.

A3.3 Overview of computer systems

The main application used by the company is the accounting and costing system. This is regarded as being of particular importance and which 'it would be difficult to do without'. This is a construction specific accounting package which was installed about two to three years ago following a review of their system.

The application considered to be next in importance is the Performance Reporting System. This tracks and maintains information about all contracts, their cost, value and profitability. As a management support system, this too is considered 'essential for the business' to provide accurate information to monitor and control profitability, and forecast expenditure.

There is a central estimating department which uses a computer based estimating system. This has been in use for about five to six years and although used by over half the estimators, it is by no means universally accepted. Spreadsheets are also used as an estimating aid. About 70% of tenders are prepared using a computer system. A post contract module is available with the estimating system although this is not currently in use, however its implementation is being considered.

Other computer-based systems are used for, general office applications, word-processing, project planning, engineering analysis and design and, recently, CAD.

A3.4 Computer systems in detail

A3.4.1 Performance reporting system

In 1988 external consultants were commissioned to carry out a systems strategy review to make recommendations for the development of a strategic framework and to identify areas of short-term improvement. This study identified the need to design and implement an integrated management reporting system.

This is a system intended to integrate and draw together information from several sources so that it can provide management with a full picture of the performance and profitability of the whole operation. It gathers information from the following sub-systems:

- Cost Value Comparison
- Forecast to Completion
- Notification of Application
- Cash Received
- Claims Remaining/Forecast

It was agreed that a development of this type should be put in hand, and as it was of major importance to the organisation, cost was not considered to be a critical issue. The consultants arranged for the design and implementation of the system. Due to the priority and importance given to it, no benefit study was carried out. The original cost was anticipated to be in the region of £20,000 for the complete hardware and software implementation, which was to be completed during a 12 month period. The system was developed using dBaseIII on DOS-based hardware. It took twice as long to complete and cost three times as much as was originally estimated. The system is currently being rewritten in-house on the RECITAL database running under the UNIX operating system.

Even though the cost of the system was considered not to be of major importance, there seems to have been little attempt to manage the IT implementation, and control the cost. However the provision of improved management information allows directors and senior managers to make more informed, and hopefully better, decisions to increase the profitability of the organisation. It is considered difficult to quantify the benefits from implementing this system; and to evaluate any losses caused by the delay in delivering the system on time.

A3.4.2 Construction project planning

A project planning package was purchased about eight years ago. At that time a small number of potential packages were considered, however it seems unlikely that any cost/benefit study was carried out, and no procedures were used to quantify any benefits of implementing a system. The main driver behind the decision to go a certain route and choose a specific package appears to have been the previous use and experience of systems by one of the planners who would be using the system. The experience of potential users is one of the parameters that should be considered when purchasing any system since a previous user is likely to require less training than one who has never used the system before.

Since the system was purchased, many more project planning packages have become available. Software engineering techniques and product development has meant that some systems have more functionality, and the introduction of improved graphical user interfaces (GUI) makes them easier to use. Within the company planning staff has changed, with the original planners having moved or left the organisation.

This has meant that staff have questioned whether the planning package used is the right one today. Although it has the functionality required for complex jobs, it can appear cumbersome and over complicated for the simpler projects. Some of the planners wanted to have the ability to quickly create bar charts for a project, rather than spend time using a complex package with facilities that were not required.

At a similar time, two projects were started where the client had specified the use of another project planning system. This seemed to provide a possible solution and accommodate the planners, need for a simpler system. It was decided to use this package on the two projects concerned to evaluate them. No cost benefit studies were carried out since the specification by the client was considered to be a good reason to use the software.

These projects have now been completed, but the experience gained using the packages proved inconclusive. However the package has now started to be used for other projects and appears to have become established as an alternative planning system.

A3.4.3 Plant management

Although not identified by the 1988 strategy review a new plant control system was specified, designed and developed by the external consultants responsible for that review. There was some consideration given to the cost aspects of a new plant management and control system, but no evidence of any cost/benefit study.

Both the plant and accounting departments were involved with the system specification, although there is now some criticism both about the computer system itself and the information provided. In addition to errors having been identified in the algorithm used to deal with depreciation of plant items, the reporting facilities are inadequate for current requirements. Data is transferred from the plant system to a spreadsheet for manipulation and some report presentation. It would appear that although the system implemented does not provide the necessary reports, it is likely that changes in accountancy staff has meant that different or additional reports are required that were not originally specified.

A3.4.4 Accounting and costing

The company ran a construction accounting system based on a mini-computer for many years. About four years ago it became clear that this system was approaching the end of its life, spares were becoming difficult for the hardware, and the software house had indicated that they were no longer able to support the software. There was obviously no alternative but to upgrade to a new system from the same supplier, or to look elsewhere. Since the option of returning to a manual system was not considered to be realistic. The use of a computer bureau was rejected because the company wished to keep in-house control of the computing facility.

External management consultants were employed to advise on the selection and choice of an appropriate system. The company initially identified 12 possible contenders, this was quickly reduced to five, and subsequently three, including the supplier of the existing system. An in-company working group of three were tasked with looking at these and making recommendations to the Computer Steering Group. It has already been stated that the company feels a computer based accounting system is of major importance to the organisation and that 'it would be difficult to do without it'. For this reason, no study was done to quantify the benefits.

A specification and supplier questionnaire was prepared and results considered. The working group visited the software houses, had demonstrations and working sessions. Following an extensive evaluation exercise, the working group made recommendations that the company should change to another system. The decision was based on the user interface with the proposed system seeming to be more friendly; the history of support on the existing system, and the hope that a new supplier could provide better support; and the cost of the system, the recommended solution would cost £20,000 less than the other main contender.

The new system was installed about three years ago, the change went well with few problems. The main concerns were that the necessary bespoke developments were not carried out as quickly as was anticipated, and that the report generation facilities were inadequate. Both these issues have now been addressed. The old and new systems were parallel run for a period of one month and the old system maintained until the end of the financial year.

A3.4.5 Computer aided draughting

The most recent acquisition was the purchase of two PC-based CAD workstations. A cost/benefit study was carried out for the use of CAD, however it was not found possible to justify purchase on cost benefits alone. Aspects considered important in the decision to purchase the systems were:

- the ability to produce drawings more quickly and particularly where standard or repeated detailing is used,
- the speed of revising drawings as changes are received,
- the accuracy of drawings and their presentation and appearance,
- the need to be seen to keep up with other similar civil engineering companies and competitors,
- staff satisfaction and retention,
- clients' increased awareness of CAD facilities,
- the potential for marketing and the ability to impress clients.

A3.5 Conclusion

The company obviously intends to move forward with their use of computing within the organisation, however this appears to be with the reluctant support of some senior managers who depend on pressure coming from the users. One user view expressed was that management took a pragmatic approach to implementing information technology, whilst another thought some senior managers 'rather reluctant', it was also thought helpful that there were no 'IT junkies' within the organisation. Training for information technology would seem to be very much at a system level, where instruction is given or sought. There seems to be a reactive rather than a proactive approach to training.

It is generally accepted within the company that package solutions should be implemented wherever possible, however some of the existing bespoke systems are being rewritten in-house.

External consultants were used in the late 1980s to carry out the strategy review, following which, concern was expressed about the merit of allowing the same consultants to develop and implement the systems.

Although the company procedures clearly state the intention to quantify the business benefits wherever possible, when computer systems are to be implemented, it is not clear that this is done in any formalised way for presentation to the computer steering group. In most cases considered in this study there appeared to be reasons why the benefits of implementing the systems were not formally quantified, such as client specification or overriding business need.

Appendix 4 Civil engineering contractor (2)

A4.1 Introduction

It was decided that the implementation and use of IT on a larger joint venture (JV) project might pose different problems from a normal building or civil engineering contractor, and that the study should look in more detail at how one of the current joint ventures dealt with the IT aspects to site management. The project chosen for this study has a value in excess of £150m, and is planned for a four to five year duration. There are two joint-venture participants.

By their nature joint-venture projects are generally high value, the contractors wanting to share the risk and draw on the expertise of each of the joint-venture participants. Joint ventures have more autonomy than a project run by a single company and are set up as separate units, somewhat detached from the main companies. Frequently companies will be established for the duration of the project and will therefore required to maintain their own financial and statutory accounting, and other procedures.

It is therefore necessary for the JV participants to set up the complete company infrastructure before the project starts. The following organisational chart shows the management structure set up for this project.

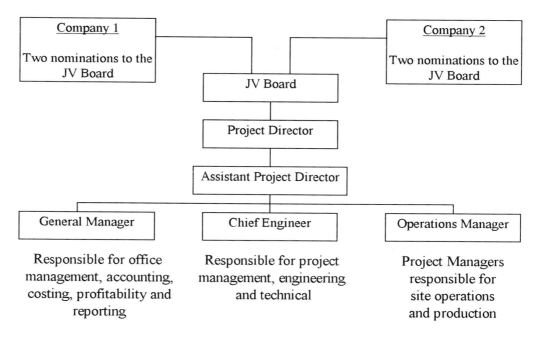

The nature of the project meant that, in addition to the main site and office complex, there are two smaller offices at remote locations and these require communication links. Due to the complexity of the project there was a lengthy pre-contract stage and considerable changes requiring modification of the estimates and project plans.

A4.2 Overview of computing strategy

A new JV project gives the participating companies the opportunity to look afresh at the various systems they are both using and to see whether they are suited to the new project, or whether other systems should be implemented. Both companies had worked together on previous joint ventures, so were aware of some of the systems they each use, but needed to review these. There was no attempt to simply transfer the systems used on previous JV projects to this project.

Following some initial investigations a detailed study was carried out led by a representative from one of the companies IT staff and involving both organisations, the site staff and users. This study was to produce a formal computing strategy for the project, and to prepare a feasibility study and cost and benefit information so that the joint venture board could discuss the issues and decide on the systems to be implemented.

Certain criteria needed to be borne in mind; the systems needed to meet the clients electronic data transfer requirements, they should support the current working practices of the joint venture partners, provide a low risk solution that would be available immediately, with the minimum of development. It was also important that before a system was implemented it should be seen to add value to procedures previously carried out.

The feasibility study:

- identified the systems needs for the project, set down the functional requirements for these systems and the interfaces between them and other external systems;
- set down proposed solutions, costs associated with them, and a timescale for implementation; and
- summarised the potential savings through benefits of implementation.

A cost benefit study was prepared for all aspects of the computing and IT investment. The main aspects included were:

- telecommunications
- central file server
- personal computers
- document management
- accounting
- project planning
- cost control system, and
- training.

the costs associated with system management were dealt with separately. It was anticipated that an IT Manager would be needed either in a full or part-time capacity.

Costs were calculated for both the initial capital expenditure and the monthly running costs. The potential benefits were identified and values given to the possible savings. These potential savings were factored by a percentage indicating the level of confidence that the savings could be achieved. The confidence levels are summarised below:

Area of Saving	Confidence Level
Telecommunications	75%
Document Management - saved copying etc.	50%
Electronic Interchange - savings in staff, post, etc.	25%
Accounting system - staff saving	50%
Reduced metal wastage	20%
Labour efficiency	20%

The likely savings were then compared with the anticipated cost in a summary of the cost benefit study. It was considered acceptable that IT costs should be paid for in full from savings during the life of the project, and hoped that a return on investment of at least 10% could be achieved.

The Project Director has overall responsibility for running the site, but the decision to proceed with the implementation of the computer systems was taken by the joint venture board. At the start of the project an IT 'champion' was nominated to promote the computing implementation and to ensure that the possible savings were realised in practice. Unfortunately in practice his other duties have meant that he has not spent the necessary time to analyse inefficiencies and modify site operating procedures to utilise the capabilities of the IT infrastructure and systems.

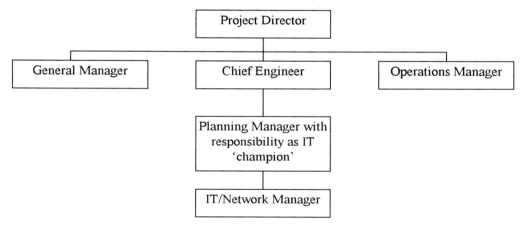

There is currently a full time IT Manager who is responsible for implementing and maintaining the computer network, infrastructure and systems, for the day to day running of the computing facilities, and to carry out some in-house training. It is likely that his role will reduce as the project progresses.

A4.3 Overview of computer systems

It was decided that since the project would run for four to five years the site offices would be provided with a fairly high degree of computing and an infrastructure that could develop during the life of the project.

The various computer systems would not be fully integrated, but should operate in each functional area, accounting, surveying, time, attendance, etc. However other users should where necessary be able to access each system and use that information.

The two aspects of communications and document management were considered to be of major importance, and it was decided to install a full communications network around and between offices, and to set up a computer-based document management system.

A structured wiring system has been installed to carry both telecommunications and the computer network. All offices were wired at the start of the project to give maximum flexibility for the use of all the offices which inevitably change their use during the life of a project. In addition to the main office and site, there are two smaller offices at remote locations requiring communications links and access to many of the systems used at the main site. The remote offices are connected by leased lines.

A computer-based document management system was set up to maintain keyword information about each document, and a scanned image of documentation taken so that they can be accessed and shown on screen.

A4.4 Computer systems in detail

A4.4.1 Project planning

Extensive project planning was done during the pre-contract period and much of this had been passed to the client for their use. The client is using a different planning system from the contractor, but data has been successfully passed between the two systems.

A third project planning system is now being used by the contractor to link time with cost, thus enabling comparison of the programme with progress monitoring and cost.

A4.4.2 Financial management

The decision was taken to implement the financial accounting system used by one of the JV companies. The only other system considered was that used by the other company. No formal study was carried out to quantify the benefits of using any particular system, however the prompt start on site did mean that they needed to implement a known system with ready access to support and training.

This system provides all the financial requirements for the production of statutory information, together with a site cost management system it provides cost monitoring information on a regular basis.

A4.4.3 Time and attendance

A computer-based system is being used to record details of attendance on site. This system uses 'swipe cards' and incorporates a photograph of the employee. It has the added advantage of being used by security, although it is not specifically seen as a security system.

A study was carried out to compare the cost of implementation of the system with a traditional method of time keepers recording the attendance information. Even though the system and set-up costs were in the region of £40-£50,000, substantial savings were identified by employing less staff. The system is intended to be used for all staff on site, both operatives and office staff, but has yet to be fully implemented.

A4.4.4 Document management

As already stated, effective document management is seen as an important issue, and a decision was taken to install a computer-based system with keyword access and scanned images of correspondence, etc. A similar system has been piloted on another site and it was decided to use the same system on this site.

The original intention was to limit those who had access to the information and to implement a single user system, but to extend it to all office staff as the technology and available facilities improved. There have, however, been some problems with the system which have not yet been resolved. Scanning correspondence is about five weeks behind which makes any use historical rather than for day to day use.

Document management systems with imaging capabilities are as yet little used on construction projects. This system is seen as being implemented for general use in the longer-term. The benefits of such a system would be the more efficient storage, access and retrieval of information which would improve decision making processes, it would also help with the archiving of documents.

A4.5 Conclusions

A4.5.1 Legacy systems

When organisations look to review their use of computers they will usually find that systems already in use restrict their freedom to choose new systems. It is perhaps surprising to find that even a project of this type (self-contained, joint venture) is influenced so much by legacy systems and the computer systems that were used pre-contract. Both the estimating system and the project planning system used during the preparation of the estimate and subsequent lengthy pre contract negotiations and planning phases are being used during the contract period. Because of the complexity and quantity of information built up in both estimating and planning systems, it was considered not to be feasible to transfer to other systems. Not only would the transfer of data be time consuming, there would be the likelihood of errors and potential loss of confidence, particularly with the client.

A4.5.2 Risk management

Effective management of the computer implementation was identified in the feasibility study as being of major importance. It was suggested that this should be dealt with by monitoring the potential risks through regular management meetings. The following 'top ten risks' were identified, although they are not presented in any specific order as it was envisaged that the priority of risks would change throughout the life of the project:

Risk	Risk Reduction
The predicted cost savings will not be realised	The cost savings must be managed. Measurements must be taken of the costs and monitored. A champion must be identified who is convinced that savings are possible and will drive them through.
The actual spend will exceed the planned spend	The system has been divided into packages. Firm quotes have been obtained for each package. The suppliers will be responsible for the delivery of a working sub-system, not a series of components. Control must be exercised over IT spending by site that lies outside the scope of this proposal.
The technology will not fit the site operating procedures	It is important that the site staff explain clearly what they want the document image processing and cost monitoring system to do. No development will be carried out until this information is available.
The users will reject the technology	The users have been interviewed about their requirements. They will be kept informed about what is being proposed and involved in commissioning. Training will be given in unfamiliar systems. The network manager will be responsible for monitoring the use of the technology and detecting signs of rejection.
The user will not be able to operate the technology	Training will be given. Packages have been chosen that are industry standard packages. Windows packages have been selected where possible.
The technology will fail	All the technology is proven and in use elsewhere in the JV companies or other construction companies.
The technology will become obsolete	There will undoubtedly be new products on the market that will look more promising. However, unless a clear cost benefit can be shown, these will be deferred for another project.
New requirements will emerge	Each new requirement will be treated in isolation. A feasibility study and cost benefit analysis will be carried out. If a clear cost benefit can be shown new facilities or sub-systems will be added.
Users will spend too much time 'playing' with the system	Management control must be exercised. In addition, the network manager must be proactive in ensuring that users do not reinvent the wheel in terms of document formats, report formats, etc.
Users will stop thinking for themselves	The site operating procedures must enforce a number of activities that force staff to think about the effectiveness of their work. These procedures must require manual work that cannot be done on the system.

A4.5.3 User expectations

The project was visited about six months after the start on site. Although the IT infrastructure had been installed, many of the systems were only partially implemented, causing some frustration to the users. This was starting to create a loss of confidence in the computing facilities since user expectations had been raised that this was to be a 'high tech' site, even though many of the computing facilities were not intended to be in place for all users from the start of the project.

Appendix 5 Consultant (1)

A5.1   Introduction

This case study is based on a large UK civil and structural engineering consultancy. The firm has a number of regional offices, each of which offers a wide range of services to local clients, as well as centralised offices dedicated to more specific services and types of work.

The total group income for 1993 was £47M and in the same year, the IT budget was £1.8M. This organisation therefore spends 3.8% of income on information technology and information systems. This is above the median figure of 1-1.5% of fee income found by the '*Building on IT for Quality*' survey.

The organisation has a split IT management structure, with one Computer Manager responsible for the northern offices and another one responsible for the southern offices. The two Computer Managers, who oversee the IT for the regional offices in their area as well as the centralised IT at the main offices, report to the Executive Director responsible to the main board for IT.

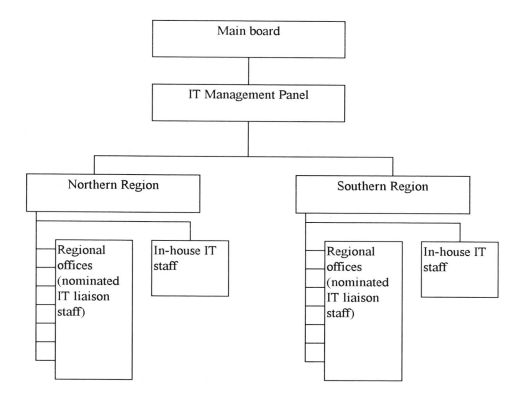

A5.2 Overview of computing strategy

There is an IT Management Panel which includes the two Computer Managers and the Executive Director for IT. The Panel is responsible for co-ordinating the Group IT Policy and Strategy.

IT can either be purchased for a particular project (it may be requested by the Client) or as a Group overhead purchase. In general, it is easier to obtain authorisation for IT which is required for a particular project. This reflects the overall strength of business needs as a driver for IT.

All software is purchased on a Group licence, even if only for an individual project. This means it is available throughout the Group for later use, if the need arises. The extra cost may mean that the purchase has to be written off over a number of projects, rather than just one, which introduces the risk that suitable projects on which to use it may not be forthcoming.

The fact that project specific IT is usually requested by the client has meant it has been difficult not to amass a broad range of different software packages. This has the advantage that the experience of the Group in using different packages expands. As the library of in-house software increases, it becomes more likely that any specified package is already within the Group, thus reducing the project start-up costs. However, a wide range of software means it is difficult to have a clear Group strategy for using particular packages and presents problems in keeping abreast of updates, both in terms of time and money.

There are company procedures which require those who encounter problems and think an IT solution is appropriate to put a business case for the purchase of the necessary hardware and software. All requests for IT solutions are routed through the Computer Managers, who will appoint one of their staff to look at the problem and the sensibility of any suggested solution.

There are a number of levels of expenditure for which there are different, and more rigorous, authorisation protocols. At the lowest level, the approval of a Computer Manager is sufficient. The intermediate level requires the agreement of the IT Management Panel. Finally, large investments are put to the full Board for approval.

A5.3 Overview of computing systems

The consultancy runs a combination of minicomputers, attached to terminals and some PCs, workstations and stand alone PCs. Of the PCs, approximately 30% are networked on local or wide area networks.

In addition to the basic business functions of word processing, database and accounting, the consultancy has a comprehensive array of other software tools both in relation to the basic core business (specifications, CAD, structural analysis, bills of quantities) and the expected additional skills of electronic publishing and project management.

Development of new systems is almost always from an external software house or through purchase of off-the-shelf systems.

Networking is used extensively within head office, less so in regional offices or between offices. There is no networking on site or between sites and offices. Both electronic mail and electronic data interchange are moderately used between and within offices. EDI is also used with external organisations.

A5.4 Examples of IT introduced to the organisation

A5.4.1 Computerised street roadworks register

This computer system was introduced to deal with new legislation and to allow the consultant to process the 30,000 notices received each year from the utilities involved in carrying out roadworks.

The specification for the system was established by the internal project manager and included the following considerations:

Functionality - the system needed to satisfy the requirements of the legislation, but a positive decision was taken to limit this to the perceived actual needs and not introduce facilities that were not actually required;
User-friendliness - it was important that users would like using the system, as this was seen as a key to its successful implementation;
Cost was an issue, but as a budget had already been set and was ringfenced within the organisation, it was not an overriding issue.

For the implementation of the system, a period of initial training was allocated to bring the new staff recruited to use the system up to speed. Training for new staff subsequently has been by existing staff.

One consideration in the choice of systems was the number of staff required in the department to operate it. This was estimated and taken into account, but was not calculated scientifically.

Unexpected benefits from the system have been the formation of a user group for the software, which is used to generate updates to the software. The chosen system is also based on a geographical information system and links into the existing GIS used by the consultant. In addition, the department has benefited from running training courses in the software for other users.

No formal post implementation audit of the system or comparison of the benefits it has delivered has been carried out.

A5.4.2 CAD

The CAD systems operated by the department are MOSS, GDS and LEAP, all run on VAX minicomputers operating as client servers to workstations. This is currently being re-evaluated and compared with using these applications on PCs entirely. This is justified as PCs are nearly equivalent to the existing workstations in terms of performance.

As the department has recently been acquired by the consultant, there is a period of general rationalisation towards the corporate IT strategy.

The benefits of introducing CAD to the organisation have not been quantified. There is an improvement in overall productivity when taken over the life of a drawing. The initial production may not necessarily be quicker than drawing by hand, depending on the complexity and level of detail. However, producing revisions is much quicker and can provide a significant saving when drawings go through many revisions.

A5.4.3 Transport modelling

Transportation planning is a very heavy user of IT, and could not realistically function without it. The applications that are used are specialised.

The purchase of the necessary systems and the associated training has been funded entirely by the project budget. The transportation department has knowledge of suitable software products that are on the market and makes recommendations to the IT department. Managers may also make suggestions for appropriate hardware, but would take the lead from the IT group. This is to maintain compatibility within the Group of hardware and, where possible, software.

The need for new or improved software comes from the business managers looking at the projects being and likely to be undertaken by the consultancy - the wide selection of software purchased by the Group for various contracts has expanded the business horizons in the range of work that can be taken on.

The need for new hardware comes mainly from users, in terms of the performance of their systems.

A5.5   Perspective from a regional office

The previous paragraphs of this case study have given the perspective of a department within the head office. Equally important is the devolution of IT to regional offices.

Each regional office has a nominated IT supervisor. This individual is not an IT professional and has a standard engineering role within the consultancy. The IT supervisor provides a link between the regional office and the Computer Manager and his staff in the main office. The IT supervisor used to be at technician level within the office, however, this has been upgraded to a person at Principal Engineer level and he or she is expected to look forward to future needs, as well as assessing previous decisions.

A significant problem with the use of IT is the ability to keep up with the revisions to the software packages. With software that is acquired for a specific project, but is kept by the Group, it may not be needed or used for several months or years, during which one or more upgrades may have taken place, which require both physical implementation and staff training.

The use of cost benefit analyses has declined within the Group since the initial introduction of computers to engineering consultancy. At that time, IT was a straightforward replacement for manual operations, and a detailed analysis, taking account of time savings, staff costs etc. could be made.

The IT investments made now are ones which are driven by the business needs of the Group, enabling the Group to offer new services to its clients, so no direct before and after comparison is possible. Investments are frequently made on the basis of perceived expectations rather than rigorous analysis, and involve much more intuitive judgement. However, on major investments, a full costing profile is carried out. This treats the IT system as a business proposition and compares costs with predicted income from increased efficiency (for replacement systems) or fees earned from services. Even so, the benefits are not always as predicted, however other unexpected benefits accrue which justify the investment as a whole.

There is seen to be a problem of training and awareness of IT at Director level (both board and divisional directors) within the Group. One effect of this is a lack of understanding of the implications of decisions or the difficulty of carrying out some operations whose benefit may in the end only be marginal.

To sum up, whether or not it can be justified in purely financial terms, investment in IT simply cannot be avoided.

A5.6 Conclusions

The Group operates two distinct philosophies with regard to IT acquisition, and hence to the degree to which questions regarding the benefits are asked.

At the overhead level, software and hardware is strictly specified to ensure compatibility with company standards.

At the project level, the group will accommodate (within reason) any requests for particular hardware or software specified by the client, if these can be written off to the project or a series of projects. In order to maximise the possible usage of any particular piece of software, this is bought under a Group licence.

The analysis of benefits is much more apparent at the overhead level, although rigorous, quantitative analyses are only carried out in exceptional circumstances, when very large investments are being made. At project level, the specification of the client is reason enough to purchase the necessary items of hardware or software.

Appendix 6 Consultant (2)

A6.1   Introduction

This case study is of a top ten multi-disciplinary engineering consultancy practice having both a regional UK structure and a number of overseas offices and contracts. The consultancy practice had an annual turnover in FY 1992/93 of £41m. A Policy Group, equivalent to a Board of Directors, is supported by management groups with responsibilities for finance, personnel, marketing and information systems. The Chairman of each of these groups sits on the Policy Group.

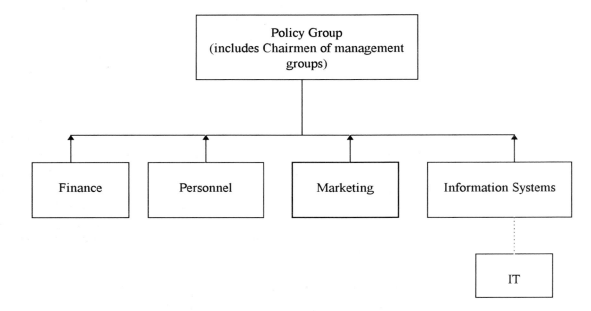

A6.2   Overview of computing strategy

IT is a central service with two senior IT managers and a number of technical and maintenance staff within the department to give a total of 12 people. In addition a Partner has an overall responsibility for IT/IS, chairing the IS management group and representing IT/IS on the Policy Group.

The arrangements for IT can be summarised as:

- central co-ordination
- central control over expenditure
- central purchasing guidelines
- strategic management through the IS management group
- monthly reporting of progress
- discipline groupings of views and experts
- consultation with key discipline group representatives and across offices
- fault rectification by central services
- central software co-ordination and Quality Assurance records

The purchase and specification for new systems, hardware and software purchases is subject to central guidelines and control. By operating this way, the practice has a broader picture for IT and IS; setting the budget for IT around needs, or anticipated needs. These needs, though identified by the IT section, are agreed through the management structure shown previously and are a response to both formal (structured interview with each office) and informal consultation and feedback in-use. The advantage of this principle is that it is not necessary to justify every purchase. However in each case, a view is taken by the IT section, again in consultation where appropriate, on the efficiency of the purchase. To illustrate this, one section requested a monochrome plotter for a particular project. The request put up to the IT section for authorisation asked for the cheapest plotter that would do the job. The purchasing decision though was for a higher specification mid-range machine because:

- the section's requirements would soon exceed the capabilities of the cheaper plotter as the ability to produce high-quality plotted output encouraged demand.
- a wider demand for similar output from other groups meant that a number of machines were likely to be purchased over a relatively short period and it was desirable to standardise on one particular type and specification.

Further illustrations of how this principle works in practice are given in relation to specific systems, below. However, it is worth highlighting at this stage that the philosophy adopted attempts to achieve a balance between overall IT infrastructure development and immediate project needs. To enable the total resources of hardware and software to be managed more effectively, items are moved about within the company without the restrictions imposed by 'virtual' ownership. This can arise when a piece of hardware or software is purchased with a project budget and continues to be felt after the project has finished. A small pool of equipment for internal rental has been created to simplify decision making for short term project needs.

The trend is for PC Networks being integrated with the current VAX Network to provide the full range of IT communication tools.

A6.3 Overview of computing systems

A6.3.1 Procurement and cost/benefit assessment

As discussed above all new systems and software are procured centrally by the IT department and charged to the overhead of the organisation rather than being assigned to particular projects. When selecting systems there is an involvement either implicitly (through the management groups and consultation) or explicitly of all levels and interested parties in the process. Each of the following groups have specific requirements and concerns which need to be met:

Partners	cash flow and overall expenditure on IT
Senior Management	business performance; commercial competitiveness
IT Staff	compatibility; maintenance; fitness-for-purpose; cost
Project managers	project specific performance suitability
Users	usability; practicability; task specific performance.

There is no formal cost-benefit appraisal as it is considered too complex with the variety of criteria listed above. All purchases are monitored through the IT department to establish whether they perform as expected. This is judged by seeking consensus opinions on efficiency from the different groups, as above, in achieving their objectives. Normally the consensus is clear-cut. This approach is appearing to be successful as business performance has continued to improve.

The benefits from developing IT/IS seen as most relevant to the business are:

- competitive pricing
- improved quality (CAD outputs)
- better communication (networking between offices)
- more flexibility (sharing information)
- consistency of information and better management of information
- ability to change more quickly and to manage and track the changes.

Difficulties faced include:

- keeping up-to-date on technical specifications and cost
- selecting those technologies which would, in the end, make a significant impact
- defining fitness-for-purpose
- avoiding the distraction of certain long-term anticipated advantages which were unrealistic.

A6.3.2 Software developments

With the exception of the account and financial systems, off-the-shelf software is now used for the majority of technical and administration tasks. The support offered by many of the software houses in terms of on-line help and updates means it is no longer cost-effective to carry out in-house development.

The accounting and financial system was developed in-house although the standards of off-the-shelf systems has now improved to the extent that the same decision is unlikely to be made again.

In place of in-house developers, a number of staff from the various offices are identified as technical champions from whom advice is sought by the IT department and who provide testing, comparisons and technical auditing of new packages.

A6.3.3 Networking

This consultancy sees networking as being able to deliver the significant benefits from IT/IS investment. However, early experience was painful. A small network was implemented five years ago but failed mainly through, at that time, technical inability to service it. Since then, the systems for networking and for network management have moved forward dramatically and those who were involved with the initial failure are now the greatest advocates for networks. Although the initial attempt did fail, much was learned.

A6.3.4 Technical software

Two very different systems have been particularly successful in delivering significant perceived benefits - the benefits have been qualified not quantified.

Specialist software with a dedicated purpose (e.g. design and analysis of masonry arches)

A requirement was generated by a particular project resulting in a review which identified and assessed an appropriate software package. Although the benefit justification for the purchase was related to a single project, potential use throughout the firm was considered as part of the discipline co-ordinator's review. The whole process was monitored by the central software co-ordinator, who maintains quality assurance records of all software purchases and installations. After successful use on the first project, the same software became the preferred package for the organisation. This example demonstrates the value of central co-ordination to route communications and maintain records for software packages assisted by a network of technical champions and independent auditors in many different offices.

Widely used standard packages (e.g. computer aided structural design and drafting)

An integrated design and drafting software package was introduced following a strategic evaluation by a small working party which included a draftsman, a designer, a manager and a software specialist. This working party considered the benefits and implications, both for the business and on working practices, of introducing this powerful tool and method of working. The application has proven successful, staff like the method of working and clients appreciate the standard of output and presentation now possible on a routine basis.

A6.4   Conclusions

This case study has featured a consultancy group who have taken a particular route to managing IT and IS within the organisation. The system adopted central policy implementation and control assisted by nominated IT representatives, linked through the company QA system, for each office or business and technical champions able to provide support and test drive new software.

Benefits are looked for in all purchases, which is one reason for having central approval even for relatively small items. The need to take this route can be a problem where needs are project driven, although this has been overcome to some degree by creating a pool of equipment which moves between projects. However, taking a firm-wide view, investment decisions are better made by those who are best placed to see the whole picture. This approach also avoids project team ownership, allowing, in theory and in practice, better planning and use of existing IT investments.

The organisation feels that it is now getting better value than previously from its systems. In the future, networking communications are seen as providing substantial benefits, although they have to be justified by today's expenditure producing today's benefits.

Investment in networking has become a priority policy objective for the IT/IS department in advance of improving the density and availability of computer systems.

Appendix 7 Consultant (3)

A7.1 Introduction

This consultant is an international group, with a UK turnover of £80+ million in 1994. The company includes a number of both technical and regional divisions. The IT spend for the same period was £3.9M, including hardware leasing, maintenance, software, personnel, telecommunications and a proportion of overhead costs such as accommodation, printing, etc.

The total IT budget, therefore, represents 4-5% of turnover. This figure is at the higher end of the range of values for consultants' spend on IT identified by the CICA Report *'Building on IT for Quality'*.

Group management of information technology is divided into three distinct sections, a Strategy Unit providing overall group strategy and policy, an Operations Unit for day-to-day running of systems, support and training and a Software/Consultancy Unit which provides services on a fee-paying basis. This last section is available both to other divisions and units within the Group and to external clients.

The general structure of the organisation is shown below:

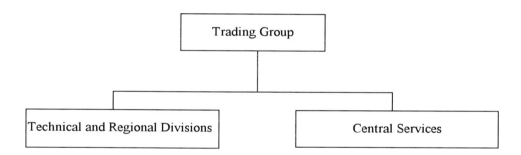

A7.2 Overview of computing strategy

Information Technology policy is set by the Strategy Unit and represented at board level by a director responsible for IT and systems. A discussion forum exists for the development of strategy.

Transfer of policy to the separate divisions is handled via normal management lines of responsibility. Computer representatives provide a divisional point of responsibility for computing as well as first line support to users.

With feedback from users, the Strategy Group has defined 'Group Standard Software' which is used for general applications, e.g. word-processing and spreadsheets.

New systems which are requested by the divisions are steered by a small working group, chaired by the Strategy Unit, including staff from the user division and staff with relevant expertise from other areas of the Group.

The individual divisions operate as autonomous business units and have their own budgets for hardware and software purchase, separate from Group Standard Software. Guidelines are laid down for hardware, operating systems and software. There is a rigid policy with regard to the networks. Where programming languages are required, there is a free choice.

The divisional manager or director must approve the procurement of divisional systems and all divisional hardware, which is then passed by the computer representative to the Operations Unit which handles the actual purchase.

Normal commercial criteria are used within each division to justify purchases.

Divisional managers are given ownership of systems that relate exclusively to their divisions and have to sign off the specification and the delivery of systems. It is also their responsibility to see that the systems are implemented properly and work well.

A7.3   Overview of computing systems

The Group has a wide range of minicomputers, workstations and PCs, from a variety of manufacturers. Eighty percent of the PCs are networked. Overall, the ratio of screens to staff numbers in different departments ranges from 1:1 down to 1:1.7.

A very wide range of software is used by the Group, including systems such as electronic publishing and document image processing, as well as more traditional office automation and technical systems such as CAD and design packages.

Electronic mail is used extensively between offices, and to a limited extent between office and site or with external organisations.

Networking is already extensively implemented, with all significant offices connected to each other, the majority of screens within each office are also networked. Approximately 50% of sites are connected to the network, and on 10% of sites, the network extends throughout the site offices.

The development of new administrative/finance systems is almost always from an external software house or supplier, using off-the-shelf packages where possible. This approach is also used for technical software. However, there is an increased likelihood that technical software will not exist elsewhere and will have to be developed in-house.

Spending on Information Technology is all on a revenue basis, i.e. costs are met from fee income rather than purchased as a capital item and written off over a number of years. Hardware is leased rather than purchased, providing additional flexibility. There is no requirement that investments in IT have to produce a given rate of return, instead divisions must be able to meet the leasing costs of systems purchased from their fee income.

A7.4 Benefits and assessment of IT systems

The benefits that were judged as being most relevant to the organisation's use of individual systems were as follows:

- competitive pricing
- giving 'competitive' edge

followed by

- reducing the time for projects
- enabling quicker response to enquiries
- better control of project information
- access to better information.

The majority of these benefits are directed towards the external appearance of the Group in how it presents itself to its clients and ensures it meets their needs. There is less emphasis on the internal workings of the organisation, and the often quoted benefit of IT that it reduces staff numbers and hence costs was assessed as the least important benefit.

There is no formal procedure that requires a cost/benefit study to be undertaken before IT systems are procured. The main reason for this is that the procurement of systems is mainly driven by individual divisions commercial needs. Amongst other things, this is based on the requirements of individual projects, through client specification.

However, there is a procedure for carrying out post-implementation audits of systems. These will either be carried out by the Strategy Unit or the individual division. This ensures that there is continuity between the success of existing systems and the assessment of new systems within the Group.

The nature of the work undertaken by the Group means there are difficulties in assessing the benefits gained from IT in a quantitative way. It is not enough simply to compare the rate of drawing production, for instance, as the differences between projects mean that like is not being compared with like. Another alternative, that of mirroring manual and automated production on the same project is not a cost effective use of resources.

It is equally difficult to accurately predict the benefits that will accrue from a particular use of information technology. In a number of cases, the choice to use IT or not does not itself exist as there is no manual method for actually carrying out the required work, for example complex finite element analysis. In other cases, although it would be possible to use manual methods, such as in accounting or production of management information, the performance requirements of the system mean this is not a viable alternative, due to cost or time constraints. Under these circumstances the need to use IT is not due to comparison between costs and benefits, rather the policy decision to offer the service or collect the information dictates that IT shall be used.

Where there are benefits to be predicted and compared, in order that the optimum solution is chosen, it is common for the achieved benefits to be different from the predicted ones, either in their nature or in their time to emerge.

The lessons of previous computer system implementations are being learnt and the proportion of systems which are successful has been increasing. No instances of systems failing to meet their objectives were given.

A7.5   Computer Aided Draughting

The Group's switch from manual draughting to CAD is used as an example of how the predicted benefits were achieved and additional benefits were also gained.

The principal benefit identified prior to implementation of the CAD system was increased efficiency in drawing production. The Group achieved this benefit, but not as easily or as quickly as had been originally thought. In the end, however, considerable benefits were achieved.

In addition to the intended benefit, there were additional benefits which were unforeseen. These were the higher quality and the consistent appearance of drawings as well as greater accuracy. However, as noted above, both the predicted and the unforeseen benefits are not able to be quantified in any meaningful way. In any case, the changes that have taken place in the industry as a whole since the Group undertook this exercise mean that it would not be possible to revert to manual draughting.

The major problem associated with the implementation of the system was the retraining of draughtsmen to acquire the new skills relevant to CAD. This exercise took much longer than had been originally anticipated and in some cases was not a success. Workforce skill level is the major human resource issue related to this type of IT implementation as the previously clear distinctions between engineers and draughtsmen are blurred by the integrating effect of computer systems on engineering design and drawing production.

A7.6   Conclusions

This case study has described a consultancy which is satisfied with the benefit it has gained from its investment in information technology and information systems. This can be demonstrated through the use of post-implementation audits. It would appear that the fact that the Group does not carry out cost benefit analyses at Group level on potential new systems for a division has had little or no effect on the success of its IT strategy.

This is partly explained by the main driver for IT investment, being client requirements and commercial pressures. In such cases, the cost of the IT in built into the fee income and no separate case has to be made beyond whether or not to accept the work if it is offered. Thus quantifying the benefits of a particular system is not a suitable line of enquiry to follow.

The organisation is satisfied that its procurement system of consulting users, through the relevant divisions and bringing in the technical expertise of the Strategy Unit is suitable for ensuring that systems will meet the commercial pressures being experienced by each division of the Group.

Bibliography

BUTLER COX FOUNDATION (1990)
Getting Value from Information Technology.
Research Report 75. Butler Cox, London.

COMPUTER FINANCE (1992)
Measuring the Intangible
APT Data Services, London, September 1992 pp 23-4

CONSTRUCTION INDUSTRY COMPUTING
ASSOCIATION and KPMG (1987-1993)
Building on IT (1987)
Building on IT for the 90s (1990)
Building on IT for Quality (1993)
Survey of IT trends and needs in the Construction
Industry, CICA, Cambridge

CONSTRUCTION INDUSTRY COMPUTING
ASSOCIATION (1991)
Building IT 2000
CICA, Cambridge

CROSS N (1992)
Promises! Promises! A paper
The Open University

DEPARTMENT OF TRADE AND INDUSTRY
(1992)
Best Practice Benchmarking: an executive guide
DTI, London

DOS SANTOS B L (1990)
Justifying Investment in New Technologies.
Journal of Management Information Systems, 7(4)
pp 215-222

DREWER and HAZELHURST
Myth and Reality in the use of IT
In *Management of Information Technology for
Construction* edited by K Mathur *et al.*
World Scientific Publishing Co. Singapore

DRUCKER P F (1988)
The Coming of the New Organisation
Harvard Business Review, January-February 1988

EARL M J (1989)
Management Strategies for Information Technology.
Prentice-Hall, London.

FARBEY B, BENSON R J and TRAINOR H E
(1993)
*How to Evaluate your I/T Investment: a study of
methods and practice*
Butterworth Heeinemann, Oxford

HENDERSON D and ELLIS P (1994)
*Effective Planning and Practical Concerns
Information Management: a director's guide*
The Institute of Directors

HOCHSTRASSER B and GRIFFITHS C (1990)
*Regaining Control of IT Investment: a handbook for
senior management*
Kobler Unit, Imperial College, London

HOCHSTRASSER B (1990)
*Evaluating IT Investment - Matching Techniques to
Projects.*
Journal of Management Information Systems, 7(4)
pp 215-222

HOCHSTRASSER B
Does Information Technology Slow you Down?
Kobler Unit, Imperial College, London

HOGBIN G & THOMAS DV (1994)
Investigating in Information Technology
McGraw Hill

HUFF S L (1990)
Evaluating Investment in Information Technology
Business Quarterly, Spring 1990 pp 42-45

PRICE WATERHOUSE (1993)
Information Technology Review
Price Waterhouse, London

KAPLAN R S and NORTON D P (1992)
The Balanced Scorecard - Measures that Drive
Performance
*Harvard Business Review, January-February 1992
pp 71-79*

KAY J (1993)
Foundation of Corporate Success
OUP, Oxford

McCARTHY D (Nov. 1994)
Cost Justifying Document Management, article in
Consultants Conspectus, Prime Marketing Publications

PARKER M M, BENSON R J and TRAINOR H E
(1988)
Information Economics.
Prentice Hall, New Jersey

PETERS G (1990)
Beyond Strategy - Benefits Identification and
Management of Specific IT Investment.
Journal of Information Technology, 5 pp 205-214

PORTER M E (1980)
*Competitive Strategy: techniques for analyzing
industries and competitors*
MacMillan, New York

PORTER M E (1985)
*Competitive Advantage: creating and sustaining
superior performance*
The Free Press, New York

PORT S (1989)
The Management of CAD for Construction
BSP Professional Books

ROWAN T G (1982)
Managing with Computers
Heinemann, London

SCOTT-MORTON M S (1991)
*The Corporation of the 1990s - Information
Technology and Organisational Transformation*
OUP, New York

SILK D J (1990)
Managing IS Benefits for the 1990s
Journal of Information Technology 4 (5) pp 185-193

STRASSMAN P (1990)
Business Value of Computers
The Information Economic Press, New Canaan.

STRASSMAN P (1985)
Information Payoff: the transformation of work in the electronic age
Free Press, New York

TAFFS D H (1985)
Guidelines on Costs of Computer Resources in the Design Office
CICA, Cambridge

WALSHE G and DAFFERN P (1990)
Managing Cost Benefit Analysis
MacMillan, Basingstoke

WARD J, GRIFFITHS P and WHITMORE P (1990)
Strategic Planning for Information Systems
Wiley

WILLCOCKS L (1989)
Measuring the Value of IT Investment
Journal of Information Technology 4 (4) pp 239-242

WILLCOCKS L and LESTER S (1991)
Information Systems Investment: evaluation at the feasibility stage of projects
Technovation, 11 (5) pp 283-302

WILLCOCKS L (1992)
Evaluating Information Technology Investments; Research Finding and Reappraisal.
Journal of Information Systems 2 (3) pp 243-268

WISEMAN C (1985)
Strategy and Computers - Information Systems as Competitive Weapons
Dow-Jones, Irwin